DID I DO THAT?

Dorothy Laux

DID I DO THAT?

Pictures by Allan Eitzen

BROADMAN PRESS
Nashville, Tennessee

© 1970 BROADMAN PRESS
Nashville, Tennessee
All rights reserved.
424–211

Suggested Classification: JF
Library of Congress Catalogue Card Number: 70–113215
Printed in the United States of America
15.O6918

Contents

1

Mike's Discovery

"Hi, Mike," Ted called from across the parking lot. "Let's go to the drugstore and get a coke."

"I'll race you on my bike," Mike called back.

"That was a close race," Ted said as they entered the drugstore.

While the boys were enjoying their drink, Mike remembered. "I've got to hurry. Mother sent me after some sugar to bake a cake. See you later."

Mrs. Mitchell hung up the phone just as Mike came bounding into the kitchen.

"Who was that on the phone?" Mike asked as he put the sack of groceries on the kitchen cabinet.

"It was Mr. Reed. He owns the hardware store in the shopping center," replied Mother. "He called to say that you had disobeyed a sign in the shopping center."

"Did I do that?" Mike asked looking surprised.

"Yes, Mr. Reed said that you and Ted were riding your bikes on the sidewalk."

"What's the matter with that?" Mike asked. "You are always reminding me to stay out of the street on my bike."

"That's right, Mike. I do remind you to ride your bike on the sidewalk for your own safety. But it is different at the shopping center," replied Mother.

"What's different about it?" asked Mike.

"Several things," Mother answered. "For one thing, there are signs posted all around the center that say, Do not ride bicycles on the sidewalk. You must obey these signs. Another thing, you might run into someone and hurt him. These signs are for the safety of everyone in the center."

"Rules, rules, rules. Everywhere I go there are rules to obey," complained Mike.

"Mike, you will discover that different rules must be obeyed in different places. You must learn to follow written rules as well as those your Daddy and I tell you," Mother said.

Mike looked discouraged. He propped his elbows on

the breakfast room table and dropped his head in his
hands. As he looked out the window Mike wondered,
"How will I ever know who and what and when to
obey?"

"I'll never get to fly to Los Angeles to see Grandmother and Grandaddy," Mike said half to himself and
half outloud.

Mother put the cake in the oven. Then she brought
her cup of coffee and sat down across from Mike.

"A penny for your thoughts," Mother said jokingly.

"I was thinking about the trip I'll probably never get to make," pouted Mike. "You and Daddy said I could fly to Los Angeles alone when I learned to obey rules and signs. I goofed again today and Mr. Reed told on me."

"Mr. Reed was only trying to help, Mike. You will have another chance. Now you have discovered why you shouldn't ride your bike on the sidewalk in the shopping center. I know you can remember to follow that rule. You have already learned to obey many others."

"I had a letter from Grandmother today. She said you could come to Los Angeles either during Easter vacation or summer vacation."

"Boy, I can't wait to go to Disneyland," Mike exclaimed.

"How soon you go will depend entirely upon you," Mother answered.

2

School Patrol

"Out of bed," called Mother as she shook Mike.

Mike groaned and asked, "What time is it?"

"Time for schoolboys and girls to be out of bed," Mother answered. "Cindy is already up and dressed."

"I can't believe school starts today. Summer just isn't long enough," Mike said.

"Hurry and get dressed. You can wear some of the new school clothes we bought last week."

Mike scrambled out of bed when Mother said this. He had been wanting to wear his new clothes since the day he got them. Moments later Mike appeared in the kitchen doorway fully dressed. "Boy that bacon smells good," he said. "I'm hungry."

"I wish I never had to eat breakfast," Cindy said.

"Everyone needs a good breakfast to start the day," Mother replied.

Dad looked up from his paper and said, "Even the newspaper is talking about the opening of school today. There is an article on the front page warning people to drive carefully and observe school zone signs. Children are reminded to obey the school patrol."

As Cindy left the table Mother called, "Remember to brush your teeth. Hurry so you won't be late for your car pool."

"Mike, when you finish breakfast, go brush your teeth and comb your hair," Mother reminded.

Turning to Mr. Mitchell she said, "It doesn't seem possible that Cindy is in junior high school. Just think, the children will be in different schools for the very first time."

Soon both children left for school. The house seemed strangely quiet as Mrs. Mitchell stood by the kitchen window washing the dishes.

As Mike neared the intersection, he saw his friend Ted on the school playground.

"Hurry, Mike," Ted called. "We have only a few minutes to play before time for the bell."

Mike glanced both ways and ran across the street.

Just before recess Mrs. Howard said, "Mike, will you please come to my desk when the bell rings?"

Mike felt important because the teacher wanted to see him. He hoped she had an errand for him to run. He wished the bell would hurry and ring.

"Mike, I have a note from the school patrol," Mrs. Howard said. "It says you did not obey the patrol signals this morning."

"Did I do that?" Mike asked. "When?"

The teacher read the note aloud, "Please tell Mike Mitchell that he disobeyed school patrol rules this morning. He failed to wait for the 'go' signal."

"Mike, the first time you disobey the school patrol you get a warning note. The next time you will have to report to the principal's office."

"I'm sorry, Mrs. Howard," Mike apologized. "When Ted called across the school ground, I looked both ways and darted across the street without thinking. Guess I just forgot school rules during the summer. I promise I won't do that again," Mike said. He was thinking again about the trip.

"Run along and play," Mrs. Howard said.

After school Mike waited to walk home with Ted. As they came to the corner Mike said, "Let's wait until the school patrol gives the 'go' signal."

3

The Touchdown That Didn't Count

"Mother, please say yes," begged Mike as he ran in the house.

"Please, Mrs. Mitchell," chimed in Ted.

"Now wait a minute. One request at a time, please. Just what is it I'm to say yes to?"

Ted explained, "My parents have an extra ticket to the professional football game Saturday night. They said I could invite Mike."

"Please Mom. I've never been to a pro football game. This is the chance of a lifetime."

"We will talk it over with Daddy when he comes home. We will call and let you know," Mrs. Mitchell promised.

"Hello," Ted answered on the other end of the line. "What did your Dad say?" he asked eagerly.

"It's a deal," announced Mike. "Tell your folks thanks for the invitation. I'll be ready to go anytime you say."

When Mr. and Mrs. Davis, Ted, and Mike arrived at the stadium, the crowd was cheering. The announcer was introducing the starting lineup. Each player ran onto the field when the announcer called his name.

The players lined up on the field. The whistle blew for the opening kickoff.

Play was exciting. The visiting team had the ball first but did not make a first down. A short kick gave the home team the ball on their own 40-yard line. The quarterback threw a long pass on the first play. The team scored a touchdown. The kick for the extra point made the score 7-0. Late in the first quarter the visiting

17

team found themselves facing fourth down on the 15-yard line. The field goal attempt was good. The score now read 7 to 3.

Early in the second quarter the visiting team marched 48 yards for a touchdown. The kicker scored the extra point. The visiting team led 10 to 7.

Excitement increased as the home team took the kick-off and went all the way for a touchdown. A player blocked the kick for the extra point. The score stood 13 to 10 in favor of the home team. Seconds before half time the visiting team kicked another field goal to tie the score.

The whistle blew to signal half time. The teams left the field.

Ted and Mike watched the bands as they marched on the field during half time.

The roar of the crowd greeted the teams as they returned to the field. Mike and Ted could hardly wait for the start of play. The teams played hard but neither scored in the third quarter.

Late in the fourth quarter the home team rallied.

"Come on," yelled Mike and Ted. "Let's go."

The halfback ran for a touchdown. The boys cheered loudly. Then they moaned. They saw a flag on the field. The referee brought the ball back down the field.

Ted turned to his Dad and said, "It isn't fair to penalize the whole team just because one person is off side."

"That is the rule Ted," Mr. Davis said. "The action of one person affects the whole team."

"It just doesn't seem right," Mike agreed. "I'll guess that player is asking himself, 'Why did I do that?'"

"There are rules for every game," Mr. Davis said. "Players must obey them or be penalized."

When the final whistle blew, the teams were still tied 13 to 13.

4

Sunday Excitement

Mike walked proudly down the hallway to his new Sunday School department. He had his Bible and his new book in his hand. Mr. Norris, his teacher, brought the book to Mike when he came to visit. Mike hoped Mr. Norris would be in the department to greet him. Mike wondered what his other new teachers would be like. He was curious about his new department. His steps quickened as he neared the door.

"Hi, Mike, glad to see you," greeted Mr. Norris. "I want you to know the other teachers in our department." Mike listened to each of their names.

The teachers helped Mike feel comfortable in his new room. As he looked around, he saw lots of interesting things to do. He read the Bible verse on the tack board: "Thou shalt do that which is right and good in the sight of the Lord." Mike already knew that verse.

He saw some girls playing a Bible game. Bob was reading *The Bible Is a Special Book*. Mike found Craig and David drawing pictures to illustrate a song.

"Mike, here is a chart listing Things to Do today. You may choose from this list," Mr. Norris said.

"I would like to work on the picture activity," Mike replied. He picked up the cards and read Work together happily, Use soft voices, Put away supplies. He read each card carefully before he matched it to a picture. Mike liked being able to choose his own learning activity.

A chord on the piano gave the children a signal to come to group time. Quickly they put away their materials and supplies and brought their chairs to join others in the group.

Mrs. Wilson directed group time. Mike liked her. She planned exciting and interesting things for the children to do. They played a get acquainted game the very first thing. It was fun. Everyone made some new friends.

"Who would like to tell what you did during activity time?" asked Mrs. Wilson. Almost all hands went up.

Bob told about the book he read. The girls shared some of the new Bible verses they learned.

"I like the way you raise your hands before speaking," Mrs. Wilson said.

"Who worked on the picture activity?" Mrs. Wilson asked.

"I did that," Mike volunteered. "I matched the words on the cards to the pictures. I'll show you." Mike held the picture and showed the card Put away supplies. He held another picture of children working on a Bible game. He matched this with the card that said Work together happily.

"Are these things we should do in our own department?" asked Mrs. Wilson.

"Yes," agreed all the children.

Work together happily
Use soft voices
Put away supplies
Keep all chair legs on the floor
Raise hands before talking
Walk quietly
Carry chairs correctly
Share our materials

"I know it is not always easy to remember rules. I will write these on a chart and put them up in our room. Some of you may like to draw some pictures to show what the rules mean," Mrs. Wilson said.

Mike thought, "This is the very first time I have ever helped make rules. I am sure I can remember to obey these."

5

A Weekend Job

"Have a good time," Cindy and Mike called as Mother and Daddy drove out of the driveway.

Mrs. White had come to stay with the children while Mr. and Mrs. Mitchell went to a convention over the weekend. Mike liked Mrs. White. She had kept him at home and at church since he was three years old. She did special things like bake cookies and pop popcorn for TV snacks.

Mike slept late Saturday. It was a crisp, cool, fall morning. The sun felt good shining through the kitchen window. Mike looked out and saw pretty colored leaves falling to the ground.

"Pancakes, my favorite breakfast," Mike said as he saw Mrs. White flip one on the griddle. Mike covered his pancakes with syrup. Suddenly he was hungry.

As Mike left the table Cindy said, "Don't forget Mother said you must rake the leaves this morning. Then you can play football with the boys."

"I don't want to rake leaves," Mike said. "Mother isn't here and you're not my boss."

Sunday morning Mrs. White, Cindy, and Mike went to Sunday School and church. When Mike saw the Bible verse on the tack board, he felt terrible. He wondered why he had disobeyed his Mother. Slowly he read the verse again. "Children, obey your parents in the Lord: for this is right." Suddenly Mike remembered the verse he learned last Sunday. "Obey them that have the rule over you."

"Why, oh, why, did I do that?" Mike asked himself. "I wonder if this will cause me to miss my trip to Los Angeles."

After supper Dad called, "Mike, come to the den."

Slowly Mike walked down the hall. He put his hands behind his back as he entered the door.

"Mike, you did not rake the leaves like your Mother asked you to do. Is there any reason why?"

"No, sir," answered Mike. "I guess I was just too eager to play football."

"Mike, when you deliberately disobey you must be punished. You must rake the leaves tomorrow after school. The rest of the week you cannot go outside your own yard to play."

Mike thought the week would never end. He missed playing football with the boys on the vacant lot.

Mike knew that next week would be different.

28

6

Christmas Holidays

At first, all Mike could remember was the excitement
of unwrapping his Christmas gifts. Then he remembered

Ted coming over after Christmas dinner to show off his new bicycle.

Quickly Mother came to the bed when she heard Mike speak. "You and Ted had an accident," Mother said. "A Mr. Cook brought you to the hospital. Ted was pumping you on the handle bars of his new bike. Mr. Cook saw the bike as it began to wobble. Then the bike rolled off the curb. You and Ted and the bike landed in the street. Your head hit the pavement. Fortunately, Mr. Cook was driving slowly. He stopped without hitting you. The doctor x-rayed your head and leg. You are going to be all right."

"My leg hurts. Is it broken?" asked Mike.

"Yes, they will put it in a cast later this afternoon," Mother said. "The doctor says you will have to stay in the hospital for observation."

"Oh, no," wailed Mike. "That fouls up my plans for the Christmas holidays."

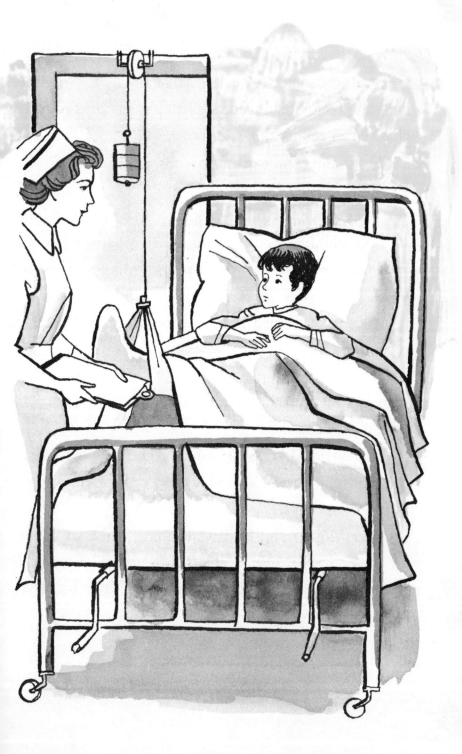

Later, the nurse wheeled Mike down the hallway. He saw a sign that read, Quiet, please. He saw other children in rooms along the way.

"Why don't some of my friends come see me?" Mike asked his Mother the next day.

"They can't," Mother replied. "A sign in the lobby says No children under 14 allowed on patient floors."

"Mail for Mike," called the nurse. Mike received lots of cards and gifts. His friends sent many games for him to play. Mike learned the rules for every new game he received.

Mother and Dad played games with Mike each night. One night Mike said, "I want to go home so I can play with my friends."

"I'm sorry, Mike," Dad said, "you disobeyed a safety rule and got hurt. Now you must stay in the hospital a few more days."

After Mother and Dad went home, Mike lay quietly on his bed. "Because I did that I probably won't be able to go to Los Angeles during the Easter holidays," Mike was thinking.

7

The Big Secret

"Whispering again!" Mike said as he entered the kitchen. "Why have you and Daddy been whispering so much the last few days?"

"We have a secret," Mother answered.

"Tell us," begged Cindy.

"Daddy will tell you tonight after supper." Mother said.

Mike and Cindy could hardly wait. They ate as quickly as they could.

"My company is sending me to a sales meeting in Florida over the Easter holidays," Daddy began. "Your Mother and I want to make it a family affair, since Mike can't go to Los Angeles."

Finally, the day came. The family loaded the car. They were off. Off to Florida.

Mike and Cindy played word games with the signs along the highway.

At noontime mother spread their picnic lunch on the table at the roadside park.

"I'm starved," Mike said as he bit into his sandwich. He looked around the park and saw a sign which he read aloud, "Place litter in trash can."

"Let's be on our way," Dad said when they finished lunch.

Driving out of the park, Cindy read another sign aloud, "Fasten your seat belt."

"That is a good safety rule to remember at all times," Daddy stated.

Mike was almost asleep in the back seat when he heard a siren. As he sat upright, he saw a flashing light.

Dad pulled over to the side of the highway and got out of the car. The highway patrolman gave him a ticket for going 70 miles an hour in a 60 mile speed zone.

"I'm sorry I did that," Mike heard Daddy say to the patrolman. "I did not know I was in a 60 mile zone."

"You will have to watch the road signs more closely," replied the patrolman politely.

As Daddy got back into the car he said, "You must all help watch for road signs. I missed seeing that one."

During the afternoon Cindy and Mike read signs that said Slow, Stop, Yield Right of Way, Do Not Pass, Speed Zone Ahead, 40 Mile Zone, No Left Turn, 30 Mile Zone, $100 Fine for Littering Highway.

As they drove up to the hotel, Mike read one more sign, Parking for Unloading Only.

Mike and Cindy explored the hotel. Everywhere they looked they saw signs. In the lobby one said, No Swim Suits Allowed in Lobby. A sign on the escalator said, No Walking on Escalator. As they came down the elevator, Cindy read a No Smoking sign.

"Let's go outside and look at the pool and beach," suggested Mike. As they walked out the door, Mike read a sign, Watch Your Step.

At the pool, the children saw several signs posted. Pool Closes at 10 p.m. No Pushing on Diving Board. Children Under 9 Must Be Accompanied by an Adult. One sign was posted both at the beach and at the swimming pool. It said Swimming Allowed Only When Life Guard Is on Duty.

"I never saw so many signs in one day," Mike told his Mother when he went back to the room.

"Rules and signs are for your own safety, Mike."

"What can we do now?" Cindy asked.

"Let's get unpacked. Then when Daddy returns we will eat supper and go to the amusement park."

"This is going to be fun," Mike said as they got on the ferris wheel.

The attendant warned, "Fasten your bar securely."

The rides thrilled Mike and Cindy. It seemed every ride had a different sign posted. Do not stand while train is in motion. Keep hands and head inside cable car. Keep in your seat until ride comes to a complete stop.

Cindy and Mike begged to ride the cable car one more time before returning to the hotel.

Back at the hotel Mike fell into bed exhausted. "This has been a fun day," Mike said sleepily. "Obeying all those signs kept us from getting hurt."

37

8

A Day for Fun

Mike walked to school in the bright sunshine. The grass along the way was turning green. The flowers were beginning to peek through the ground.

The warm, lazy days of spring made Mike know that school would soon be out.

"Boys and girls, I need your help," Mrs. Howard said. "Today we must decide where we want to go for our spring field trip on Friday. We have three choices.

This was the exciting day Mike and his classmates had looked forward to. They enjoyed planning field trips. Mike liked making choices.

Mrs. Howard listed on the chalkboard:

A Tour of the Bakery

A Trip to the Zoo

A Visit to the Museum

The children voted to take the trip to the zoo. They all started making suggestions at the same time.

"Just a minute," suggested Mrs. Howard. "We must take turns. We will leave on the school bus about ten in the morning and return at two p.m. Each of you will need to bring a picnic lunch. Now, let's think of some other things we will want to remember."

"The driver will want us to act nice on the bus," said Ann. "He has some signs on the bus that tell us what to do. One says, Do not talk to the driver."

"Another says, Keep head and hands inside the bus," added Ted.

"We will choose partners for the day. You must stay

with your partner and with our group at all times," Mrs. Howard said.

The children pressed their noses to the windows as the bus pulled into the parking lot at the zoo. The driver reminded them to remain seated until the bus stopped.

Immediately the group headed for the monkey cages. Everyone took turns feeding peanuts to the monkeys. The children laughed as they watched the monkeys swing by their tails and turn flips in the air. Mrs. Howard said it was time to move on. Ted still had a few peanuts left in his sack.

The big, fluffy lion roared as the group crowded close to his cage.

"We can't feed the lions," Ann said. "The sign says, Do not feed the animals."

Just as Mrs. Howard turned her head she saw peanuts fall in the cage near the lions.

"Who did that?" asked Mrs. Howard.

Ted dropped his head and answered slowly, "I did."

"The rule about feeding the lions is for your own safety, Ted. It is a good thing the lion was not close enough to chew your hand."

The children walked toward the elephant cages. They saw signs that read Keep off the grass and Stay on the walkway.

Gleefully the children watched as the mother elephant used her snout to pour water on her baby. She also used her snout to take the peanuts the children offered her.

"I'm hungry," groaned Tom. "When do we eat?"

All the children agreed they were hungry, too. They opened their lunches. It felt good to sit down on the soft, green grass and rest while they ate.

"Is everyone ready to go?" asked Mrs. Howard as she looked around. "I see some paper left near your group, Mike."

"Did I do that?" asked Mike.

"I do not know who left it," answered Mrs. Howard. "Would you please put it in the trash can?"

Mike walked toward the can. He saw the same sign he had read at the roadside park, Place litter in trash can.

The last hour passed swiftly. The children hurried from cage to cage. They saw the seals swimming over and under, up and around. The bears were curled up taking their afternoon nap. The tigers were pacing up and down. The giraffe was eating from a bucket placed on a pole high in the air. The hippopotamus was rolling over in a shallow pool of water.

When the bus stopped on the school grounds, the children all agreed the day had been fun.

9

A Surprise for Mike

"I can't believe it!" Mike shouted as he came bounding in the house on the last day of school.

"What happened? Tell me about it," said Mother.

"This morning Mr. Evans, our principal, read the list of school patrol boys for next year. He called my name. I just can't believe it," repeated Mike. He could hardly wait to tell Daddy.

"Supper is ready," Mother called from the kitchen.

When Mike sat down at the table, he found an envelope in his plate. Written on the outside was "For a school patrol boy." Quickly Mike opened the envelope. Inside he found a ticket to Los Angeles. Mike jumped up and down with joy.

"How did you have time to get this ticket after school?" Mike asked.

"We didn't," Mother explained. "Your principal called last week. He asked if we would sign a slip giving permission for you to be a patrol boy. Mr. Evans said he chose the boys who had learned to obey rules and carry out instructions."

"At last I've done it," Mike declared. "I have finally discovered that rules are for obeying."

CAN YOU DO THIS?

Here is a list of some of the PEOPLE children should obey.

Mother	Baby Sitter
Daddy	Bus Driver
School Teacher	Doctor
Policeman	Teachers at Church
School Patrol	Life Guard

(Can you think of others? If so, write them on a sheet of paper to show your teacher.)

On a sheet of paper write these letters backward to discover PLACES where children should obey.

emoh

loohcs

hcruhc

dnuorgyalp

yrarbil

gnippohs retnec

latipsoh

doohrobhgien

krap

Where do you see these SIGNS that you must obey?

Sign

Keep off grass

Do not disturb others

Don't walk

Fasten seat belt

No pets allowed

Do not ride bicycle on sidewalk

Place litter in trash can

Quiet, please

Do not feed the animals

Stop

Do not pass

Use crosswalk

Do not walk on escalator

No parking

Do not pick flowers

Yield right of way